DEATH
WITH DIGNITY
VOLUME II

DEATH
WITH DIGNITY
VOLUME II

By
Jennifer Green

Consultant in Public Health Medicine
Pontefract and Wakefield Health Authorities

Edited by Joanna Trevelyan
Deputy Editor, Nursing Times

Illustrated by Gary Thompson

Designed by Liz Terrell

NT
A NURSING TIMES PUBLICATION

First Edition 1993

Published by
MACMILLAN MAGAZINES LTD
4 Little Essex Street
London WC2R 3LF

Companies and representatives throughout the world.

Printed in the UK

ISBN 0-333-593650

CONTENTS

DEATH
WITH DIGNITY
VOLUME II

INTRODUCTION

The chaplain who reviewed Volume 1 of *Death with Dignity* remarked: 'Given that many of the staff of our hospitals also reflect the multicultural society, there should, ideally, be a section on Christianity, since many staff may not be familiar with the Christian tradition'[1].

I hope this booklet will raise awareness of the great diversity of Christian tradition; several very different Christian groups are included, together with Rastafarianism and Zoroastrianism. The book is not intended to be a treatise on comparative theology, but simply to highlight issues which may be of direct relevance to health-care staff when dealing with ill and dying patients and their families. I am aware that, within such brief articles, there may not be full accordance with the views of all readers; I intend no offence and apologise unreservedly if any is taken.

Within all religious groups there is the whole spectrum of belief and practice, from non-observance to extreme orthodoxy. Assumptions by health professionals about the importance of religion and rite for an individual must be avoided. The patient should be asked. The family should be asked. If neither is possible, the hospital chaplain will be ready to help in all circumstances, not just for his or her own denomination.

I do hope that this booklet and its companion volume will be sources of clear information and advice for those who must deal with death in their daily work.

REFERENCE
[1] Speck, P. *Death with Dignity* (book review). *Nursing Times* 1991; **87**:17,42.

Jennifer Green, November 1992

CHRISTIANITY

THE Christian religion acknowledges the divinity of Jesus Christ. Christians believe that some 2 000 years ago God became man on earth in the person of Jesus Christ. He was crucified, rose from the dead and ascended to heaven.

Approximately one-third of the world's population professes some form of Christianity. There are many different Christian churches, with differing structures, beliefs and rituals, but the concept of one God who reveals Himself as a Father, a Son and a Holy Spirit (the Trinity), is central to all Christian teaching.

Sacraments are ceremonies which, Christians believe, were ordained by Jesus Christ and confer spiritual gifts on those who receive them. Christian tradition recognises seven sacraments. Baptism, the 'essential' sacrament, marks the entry of a person into the family of Christ. The Eucharist is the 'principal' sacrament (also called Holy Communion, Lord's Supper or Mass), whereby bread and wine, symbolising the body and blood of Christ, are taken in His memory. The other sacraments are: confirmation, penance, extreme unction (anointing of the sick), matrimony and priestly ordination. Different churches vary in the importance they attach to the different sacraments, and their relevance to dying and death.

In England the established Church (which has been officially recognised as a national institution since the 16th century) is the Church of England, or the Anglican Church. Its adherents are called Anglicans. Anglican dogma is also common to the Church in Wales, the Church in Ireland, and the Episcopalian Church in Scotland. Anglicans account for only about 4% of the world's Christians, but they are the majority religious group in the UK, where some 57% of the population consider themselves to be Anglican. Moreover, Anglicanism is to be found worldwide with churches as far apart as the USA, Hong Kong, India and Ghana.

Considerations for the living

Most traditional ward practice has evolved via this church. Until a few years ago it was customary to have daily morning prayers in each ward led by the nursing staff. Most hospitals retain an Anglican chaplain who is able to offer pastoral care and comfort, and administer the sacraments. In the absence of chaplains of other faiths, the Anglican chaplain will offer similar care to other groups if requested or make suitable arrangements. Patients who are well enough may appreciate a visit to the hospital chapel.

Diet

There are no general dietary requirements, but some 'high' Anglicans (who may describe themselves as Anglo-Catholics) may wish to observe the traditional meatless Friday as a day of self-denial. Those awaiting Holy Communion may prefer to fast until after they have received the sacrament.

Care of the dying

Anglicans believe that those baptised into the Christian faith will share in Christ's resurrection and eternal life. Christian churches recognise the validity of each other's baptism. Baptism is regarded as the outward sign of Christ's love and the ceremony has deep significance for believers. The priest  makes the sign of the cross on the baby's forehead and pours water over the forehead three times in the name of the Trinity, signifying the beginning of a new life as a child of God and follower of Christ.

Baptism in infancy and childhood is associated with the naming of the child — the christening. If an infant dies unbaptised, without a naming cere-

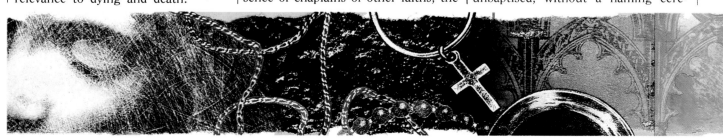

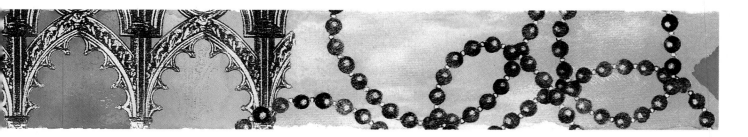

mony, the family may feel that the child has been excluded from the family of God. This may be a source of real distress to parents. For this reason, if death is imminent, baptism may be requested in emergency for babies, children or adults. In the absence of a priest, it is preferable for someone of the appropriate faith to perform baptism, but this may be done with water and in the name of the Trinity by any staff member. The priest should be informed later.

There is no age limit for baptism, and it may be performed whenever life is endangered. Should a child die upbaptised, the priest may offer a naming and blessing ceremony soon after death. This is particularly appropriate following a stillbirth, and a certificate to commemorate the ceremony may be provided.

For those already baptised, if death is imminent, the priest may be called to administer the sacrament for the sick (anointing ceremony). Holy oil is used to make the sign of the cross on the forehead, chest and wrist of the dying patients, and prayers are offered.

Hospital chaplains and other clergy will offer prayer and comfort to all who wish it, including non-believers.

Post-mortems, transplants, transfusions, and body donation

Post-mortem examinations are not forbidden on religious grounds. There is no church teaching regarding the disfigurement of a body; only the soul is believed to transcend to the next world.

There is no religious objection to the giving or receiving of blood or organs, nor to the donation of the body for teaching or research. In this last case the church would offer a memorial service after the death, and a funeral service later, when the body is finally interred.

Procedure at death

Prayers may be said at the bedside at the point of death, or over the body of the patient after death, in the ward or in the mortuary chapel. The minister offers thanks for the life which has passed and commends the soul to God's keeping.

Last offices (the washing and laying out of a body) are carried out according to normal ward practice.

Funerals

An Anglican body may be laid in the coffin with the hands crossed over the chest, placed in an attitude of prayer, or supine with the hands at the sides. Burial and cremation are equally acceptable.

ROMAN CATHOLICISM

The Roman Catholic Church is the religious body of Christians which accepts the supreme jurisdiction of the Bishop of Rome (the Pope). The Pope is acknowledged to be the true successor to St Peter, the apostle appointed by Christ to be the head of His church.

Catholics make up approximately 57% of the world's total Christian population. Probably almost a fifth of the human race belongs to the Roman Catholic faith, and Catholics constitute about 13% of the total population of the UK.

The Catholic church teaches that God is the Trinity (Father, Son and Holy Spirit), but also extols the intercessional qualities of Mary, the mother of Christ. It places greater emphasis on the sacraments and the symbolic significance of worship than do many other churches. The Catholic church teaches that this life is merely a beginning, and that death is a step to the 'fullness of life'.

Considerations for the living

Catholic patients will almost certainly wish to be visited by a priest while in hospital. Catholic chaplains regard it as

their duty to visit all Catholic patients, probably more so than do those of other Christian groups, and will usually ensure that a priest is on duty round the clock for the emergency administration of the sacraments. The presence of the priest is extremely important to patients and to their families, and health-care staff should never hesitate to call the Catholic chaplain at any time in appropriate situations.

Those patients who are well enough will wish to take Holy Communion, the sharing of bread and wine as an act of sharing with Christ. They may wish to do so regularly while in hospital and to attend the hospital chapel.

Diet
Traditionally Friday was a day of self-denial for Catholics, and became a meal-free day. British hospitals have long been accustomed to serving fish dishes on Fridays for the benefit of patients and staff, even though this is no longer considered necessary by the Church. Sick patients would not be expected to follow any dietary rules, whether at hospital or at home.

Care of dying
Baptism has great significance for Catholics of all ages. It is of particular importance that a child should be baptised before, or even at, death. A priest should be called in appropriate situations, but anyone, even a non-believer, may baptise in an emergency. A little water is poured onto the forehead of the patient, with the words 'I baptise you in the name of the Father, the Son and the Holy Spirit.' If baptism is performed by a lay person, the chaplain should be notified so the baptism can be registered.

Local addresses and phone numbers

Catholic churches

Catholic funeral directors

Catholic cemeteries

For those already baptised, the sacrament of the sick is a symbol of Christ's healing and loving. It can be adapted to the severity of the illness, and repeated if circumstances change. If the person is dying, the priest anoints the dying person with consecrated oil on the forehead and hands in a ceremony

---

(sometimes called 'extreme unction') which symbolises forgiveness, healing and reconciliation. These sacraments are of enormous signficance to believers.

Post mortems, transfusions, transplants and body donation
There is no religious objection to these but the body should be treated with reverence at all times.

Procedure at death
At the point of death, and up to three hours after death, extreme unction may be given. Routine last offices are appropriate and there is no religious objection to non-Catholics handling the body.

Funerals
Traditionally in the UK and Eire, Catholics are buried rather than cremated, but there is no religious prohibition to cremation. In some communities, particularly among Irish Catholics, it is customary to display the body after death or at the funeral — if so, the body should preferably be embalmed.

Some families, particularly Irish, Italian and Spanish ones, may wish to take the body back to their homeland for the funeral. They will require an 'out of England' certificate to do so[1].

A Requiem Mass may be held later to pray for the deceased and comfort the family and other mourners.

THE FREE CHURCHES

There are many Christian groups in the UK apart from the Anglican and Roman Catholic Churches. Some have very distinct beliefs and practices. Some churches have links with ancient mainstream churches of other countries (as,

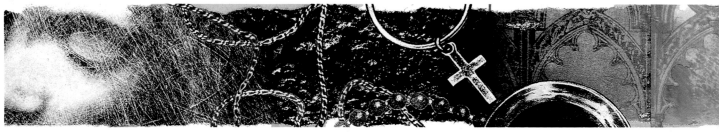

for example, the Greek and Russian Orthodox) and are subject to their control. Those churches which are tied neither to the State, nor to Rome, and which do not conform to the Anglican and Catholic tradition of hierarchial church organisation, are known as 'free' or 'non-conformist' churches and may be members of the Free Church Federal Council. Some adherents will describe themselves as Protestants or Chapel.

Free churches include the Methodist Church (at least 450 000 adherents in the UK), Baptists (170 000), the Salvation Army (some 924 churches, 139 social service centres and 1 800 officers engaged in evangelistic and social work in 1987), the Society of Friends, or Quakers, with about 18 000 members), Seventh Day Adventists (16 500 members), the General Assembly of Unitarian and Free Christian Churches, the Free Church of England, the United Reform Church and many others. The Lutheran Church has over 70 millon members worldwide, but only about 27 000 in the UK. Lutheran services in immigrant communities here are often held in other languages. All these groups have much in common despite their diversity.

Considerations for the living
The usual ward practice is unlikely to cause offence to any Free Church member.

Diet
There are no general dietary restrictions.

Care of the dying
When facing illness in hospital, or other crises, Free Church believers will usually be pleased to be visited by a minister from any Free Church, not

---

Local addresses and phone numbers

Free Churches

Free Church funeral directors

Free Church cemeteries

---

necessarily their own. A Free Church chaplain should be appointed to most hospitals in the UK. Ceremony and administration of the sacraments tend to be less important than in the Anglican and Catholic traditions, and the minister is more likely to be asked to join the patients and the family in informal prayer, rather than to administer sacraments.

For many groups, baptism of a sick infant will not be seen as essential.

Post-mortems, transfusions, transplants and body donation
There is no religious objection to any of these.

Procedure at death
For all Free Churches, routine last offices are appropriate.

Funerals
Burial and cremation are equally acceptable to most Free Churches.

REFERENCE
'Green, J. Funerals abroad. *Nursing Times* 1989; 85: 11,63.
FURTHER READING
Encyclopaedia Britannica (15th edn.) 1989 and *Book of the Year 1991*.
The Churches, *Whitaker's Almanack (Shorter Edition)*. London: J. Whitaker and Sons. 1989.
Green J.B., Green M.A. *Dealing with Death: Practices and Procedures*. London: Chapman and Hall, 1992.
Hinnels, J.R. (ed.) *The Penguin Dictionary of Religions*. Harmondsworth: Penguin, 1984.
Hospital Chaplaincies Council. *Our Ministry and Other Faiths; A booklet for hospital chaplains*. London CIO Publishing, 1983.
Neuberger, Rabbi J. *Caring for Dying People of Different Faiths*. Lisa Sainsbury Foundation Series. London: Austen Cornish, 1987.
Speck, P.W., Ainsworth-Smith, I. *Letting Go — Pastoral Care of the Dying and the Bereaved*, London: SPCK, 1982.

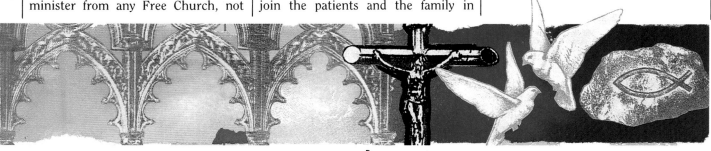

CHRISTIAN SCIENCE

THE Church of Christ, Scientist, began in 1879 in the USA. Its founder, Mary Baker Eddy (1821–1910), who suffered a great deal of ill health, experienced personal healing after reading of the healing power of Jesus Christ in the New Testament. In 1875 she published *Science and Health*, later revised as *Science and Health with Key to the Scriptures* (both available at Christian Science reading rooms). This book and the Bible form the foundation texts of the faith, which has now spread to some 60 countries. There are about 220 congregations in the UK.

The church aims 'to reinstate primitive Christianity and its lost element of healing'. Among health-care staff it is probably best known for its reliance on prayer alone for the healing of the sick. This is believed to be in line with the healing practised by Jesus Christ and is

seen as an integral part of the ministry of Christianity. Written accounts of healings appear in the many Christian Science publications, as testaments of the faith.

The Church does not attempt to control the actions of its members, who are free moral agents. It does not rebuke those who defer to family or legal pressures to undergo conventional treatment. But when someone joins the Church, it is understood that there will be reliance on God for healing, rather than on medicines or surgery. Christian Science treatment must be purely spiritual, calling for a deep understanding of man's relationship with God.

It will be unusual, therefore, for Christian Scientists to be patients in ordinary hospitals. Instead, they will usually seek nursing care at home or in a Christian Science nursing home, where treatment by prayer is administered by Christian Science practitioners. They may, however, be admitted after accidents, or during pregnancy and childbirth, and because of family or legal pressures. They will accept medical care for their children where the law requires them to do so.

Considerations for the living
If in hospital voluntarily, the Christian Scientist is likely to accept conventional, but minimal, medical treatment. He will appreciate privacy for silent prayer, with access to the books of the faith.

If the admission is not a voluntary one, the patient will normally wish to be quite free from material medical treatment. He will wish to contact a Christian Science practitioner for treatment through prayer, and to be transferred to a place where he can be cared for according to his religious convictions.

Fill in appropriate local addresses and phone numbers

Local churches

Preferred funeral directors

Preferred crematoria and burial grounds

The sacraments of baptism and communion in this faith are regarded as profound inner experiences rather than outward ceremonies. The symbols of bread and wine are not used by Christian Scientists, and there is no ceremony of any kind for a sick patient of any age.

Diet
The only dietary prohibitions are for alcohol and tobacco.

Care of the dying
Worship is kept free of ritual, and there are no last rites of any kind. Death is regarded as 'the last enemy that shall be destroyed' (1 Corinthians 15:26) and no patient is regarded as being beyond the healing power of God. Christian Science literature tells of even apparently hopeless terminal conditions which have been healed.

Post mortems and body donation
Christian Scientists would wish the body to remain inviolate.

Transfusion and organ transplantation
These are regarded as material methods of treatment and neither donation nor reception would usually be acceptable for adults. Parents would consent to transfusion for their child if doctors were of the opinion that it was essential.

Procedure at death
There are no rites at death. Routine last offices are appropriate. A female body should be handled by female staff.

Funerals
Cremation is usually preferred, but this is a matter for family choice.

FURTHER READING
Peel, R. *Spiritual Healing in a Scientific Age*. New York: Harper and Row, 1987.
Hinnels, J.R. (Ed.) *The Penguin Dictionary of Religions*. Harmondsworth: Penguin Books, 1984.
Green, J.B., Green, M.A. *Dealing with Death: Practices and procedures*. London: Chapman and Hall, 1992.

JEHOVAH'S WITNESSES

JEHOVAH'S Witnesses are deeply religious people who try to live their lives according to the commands of God, as written in the Old and New Testaments. They believe that the Kingdom of God will soon be experienced on earth. At that time God will resurrect many former inhabitants on earth, and a number who are so destined will rule in heaven with Christ. Although Jehovah's Witnesses have no belief in the Trinity, they do regard Jesus Christ as the Son of God and declare themselves to be Christians.

There are no separate clergy. All Witnesses are committed to spreading the faith, which was formalised in the USA in the 19th century and has now spread all over the world. There are about 117 000 Witnesses in the UK.

Considerations for the living

Jehovah's Witnesses are most likely to be known to health-care staff because of their fundamental religious objec-

tion to the use of blood as part of medical practice. This is founded upon teachings from the Bible which refer to blood as 'the soul of the flesh' (Genesis 9: 3–4, Acts 15:20, 28–29; 21:25) and forbid the consumption of it. These passages are taken to mean that blood must be taken neither orally nor intravenously, and this includes whole blood or its components, such as packed red cells, plasma, white cells and platelets.

Obviously, there is no biblical guidance on certain types of modern treatment, and individual Witnesses must let their consciences dictate whether to accept such products as albumin, immune globulin or clotting factors.

To Witnesses, blood represents life itself and must be handled with

respect. It is not acceptable for it to be stored or reused. Many Witnesses will accept dialysis provided that no other source of blood is used and that the extra-corporeal circulation is continuous with the body circulation. Blood samples may be taken for pathological testing as long as any unused blood is disposed of and not reused. Jehovah's Witnesses do not object to modern medicine. When ill they will seek medical advice and treatment in all respects save that of the use of blood. This is a religious belief and is fundamental to the faith.

Most Witnesses carry a small personal card which directs medical staff not to use blood or blood products as a means of treatment and releases them from responsibility in this regard. It is signed, dated and witnessed by two other Witnesses, usually a family member and a religious elder. Hospitals should have a standard form for refusal of blood which a Witness will sign for himself; a parent will sign on behalf of a child.

Baptism is unusual before the age of

12, and a young child is protected by the dedicated state of the parents and would not require urgent baptism, even *in extremis*. Baptised parents will not give consent for a blood transfusion for their child, which they regard as against biblical teaching.

The emblems of the bread and wine, representing Christ's body and blood, are taken only by those Witnesses who know that they are of the heavenly calling. The ceremony, the Memorial, takes place only once a year, on the anniversary of the death of Christ. These sacraments are thus rarely likely to be administered in a hospital environment.

Diet
There is a dietary prohibition against blood and against the consumption of animals that have been strangled. Each Witness takes responsibility to inquire whether blood or blood products are part of the dish offered. Black pudding, a sausage made from pig's blood, would be unacceptable, as would game that had been shot and improperly bled.

Care of the dying
Jehovah's Witnesses will want reassurance that blood will not be used against their wishes. Family, friends and elders of the congregation will wish to visit, but there is no formal ritual for the dying.

Post-mortems and body donation
The living body is dedicated to God, but the body has no particular religious significance once the breath of life has left it. Post-mortem examination or body donation would therefore be a matter for individual conscience.

Local addresses and phone numbers

Kingdom Halls

Funeral directors

Cemeteries/crematoria

Transplants
In general, there are no religious principles against transplants, and many aspects would be left to the individual to decide. Reception of components may be acceptable where no blood is involved, as with corneas. Donation of organs would likewise be a matter for individuals to decide, but, because other blood would then flow through that organ, it is unlikely that Witnesses would be willing donors of major organs.

Procedure at death
There are no particular rites at death. Routine last offices are appropriate.

Funerals
Both burial and cremation are acceptable. There is no formal written service; each is prepared as appropriate for the individual Witness. The ceremony may take place in the Kingdom Hall (the meeting place of the congregation) or at the crematorium.

FURTHER READING
Watchtower Bible and Tract Society of Pennsylvania. *Jehovah's Witnesses and the Question of Blood*. New York: Watchtower Bible and Tract Society, 1977.
Governing Body of Jehovah's Witnesses. *Blood Transfusion: Why not for Jehovah's Witnesses?* New York: Watchtower Bible and Tract Society, undated.
Watchtower Bible and Tract Society. Do Jehovah's Witnesses allow the use of autologous blood (autotransfusion) such as by having their own blood stored and later put back into them? *The Watchtower* 1989; March 1, 30.
Watchtower Bible and Tract Society. Jehovah's Witnesses: the surgical/ethical challenge. Reprinted in *Awake* 1982, June 22, 25–27, from the *Journal of the American Medical Association* 1981; **246**: 21, 2471–2472.
Hinnels, J.R. (ed.). *The Penguin Dictionary of Religions*. Harmondsworth: Penguin, 1984.
Encyclopaedia Britannica (15th edn) and *Book of the Year 1991*. Chicago: Encyclopaedia Britannica, 1989 and 1991.
Green, J.B., Green, M.A. *Dealing with Death*. London: Chapman and Hall, 1992.

THE MORMON CHURCH

THE Mormon Church, properly known as the Church of Jesus Christ of Latter-Day Saints, arose in America in the early 19th century. It has a growing membership of over 7 000 000 worldwide, with some 152 000 adherents in the UK. Their headquarters are in Salt Lake City, Utah, USA.

The Old and New Testaments of the Bible are essential scriptures for Mormons. In addition, the Book of Mormon, central to the beliefs of the church, is an account of the revelations of many prophets, whose words were written on gold plates and largely compiled by the prophet historian Mormon. Subsequently, Mormon's son, Moroni, added to the plates before concealing them in a hill where they lay for some 14 centuries.

In 1823, the resurrected being of Moroni appeared before Joseph Smith and instructed him about the plates. Smith translated the plates into the English language. The plates were then

returned to the heavenly messenger, Moroni.

The Book of Mormon tells of two great civilisations, one originating from Jerusalem in 600 BC, later dividing into Nephites and Lamanites.

The Mormon Church views the Holy Trinity (Father, Son and Holy Ghost) as separate members of the Godhead. There is a belief in pre-existence, a spirit world prior to mortal birth, but the new infant is born into this world with no memory of the previous life.

There is also a profound belief that, at some time after death, the spirit and the body will reunite and be resurrected. Life on earth is a period in which to prove oneself worthy to

return eventually to live in the presence of Jesus Christ and God the Father.

There is no distinction between priest and layman. At the age of 12, all 'worthy' males enter the Aaronic priesthood. At 14 they become 'teachers' and at 16 'priests'. They may enter the Melchizedek (higher) priesthood after the age of 18.

Family unity has great importance, epitomised by the 'sealing' ceremony at the Temple, whereby man and wife are sealed together for eternity. Children may be sealed with their parents. Family members already dead, who were not members of the church, may be baptised into the faith and sealed with their families (if they are worthy), so that they may be together after the resurrection. Death is therefore regarded as only a temporary separation from other loved ones.

Baptism marks the entry into the faith and is carried out with immersion. Children are baptised at about the

age of eight, when they are deemed to have reached the age of accountability.

Young children who are seriously ill would not require emergency baptism, and there are no special rituals associated with dying or death for any age group.

The sacrament of bread and water (Mormons abstain from alcohol) equates to the eucharist of other Christians and is performed each Sunday. All members who know they are worthy may participate.

Although it may be taken in hospital, it would not be regarded as essential for a sick patient.

General considerations for the living

Those Mormons who have undergone a special Temple ceremony wear a sacred undergarment. This intensely private item will normally be worn at all times, in life and in death. It may be removed for hygiene purposes and laundering, and for surgical operations, but it must at all times be considered private and treated with respect.

Diet

Mormons are health-conscious. They are not usually vegetarians but will eat meat sparingly, avoiding products with much blood.

There is concern over the effects of stimulants, including caffeine, and Mormons drink neither tea nor coffee. Some will avoid all hot drinks. In hospital, water, milk or fruit juice will be acceptable. Alcohol and tobacco are forbidden.

Care of the dying

Death, if inevitable, is regarded as a blessing and a purposeful part of eternal existence. There is no ritual for the dying, but spiritual contact is important. Church members will know how to

Local addresses and phone numbers

Churches

Funeral directors

Cemeteries

get in contact with their own bishop.

Members of the Melchizedek priesthood may give blessings and minister to the sick, both at home and in hospital.

'Home teachers' assist caring by offering home support and visiting church members in hospital.

Post-mortem examination and donation of the body

There is no religious objection to these and both would be a matter for family choice.

Blood transfusion

There is no religious objection to transfusion. The church encourages blood donation and makes its meeting houses available for this purpose.

Organ transplantation

There is no religious objection to donation or receipt of organs. Members are counselled that the decision is one for individuals and families to make, coupled with competent medical advice and confirmation through prayer.

Procedure at death

Routine last offices are appropriate. The sacred garment, if worn, must be replaced on the body after the toilet is complete.

Funerals

There are important symbolic references to burial in the doctrines of the church and burial is preferred, although cremation is not forbidden. The Bishop will offer solace and practical help with funeral arrangements. The body may be viewed before the funeral, with family prayers before the service, which will usually be at the church meeting house.

At the cemetery, a bearer of the Melchizedek priesthood will offer a simple prayer for the dedication of the grave site. The Relief Society, the women's organisation of the church, will assist the bereaved family in practical ways.

ZOROASTRIANISM

ZOROASTRIANS (Parsees) are the followers of an ancient religion named after the prophet Zoroaster (Zarathustra). Between 549 BC and AD 642, Zoroastrianism was the state religion of three successive Iranian (Persian) empires. It was eventually taken over by the expansion of Islam.

In the 10th century AD, some members of the faith left Iran to settle in North West India in the hope of finding religious freedom. Here they were known as Parsees (Persians). Today the largest communities are in India (92 000) and Iran (around 30 000), and it is estimated that there are about 7 000 Zoroastrians in Britain, about 5 000 of whom live in London.

Zoroastrian beliefs have influenced all the major monotheistic world religions, especially with regard to heaven and hell, resurrection of the dead and the last judgement. Their holy book, the *Avesta*, tells of two spirits. The good spirit, Spanta Mainyu, represents the forces of creation, and the evil spirit, Angra Mainyu, represents the forces of destruction. Spanta Mainyu is led by the wholly good God, Ahura Mazda, to protect the creation of Ahura Mazda which is in constant conflict with the evil spirit, Angra Mainyu.

Man has a religious duty to care for both the material and spiritual aspects of life, as both are created by God. Physical and moral purity are paramount. Worship is characterised by maintaining the temple fire. Sacred symbols include cattle, earth, water and plants.

Children are initiated into the faith at the *navjot*, between seven and 15 years old. On the initiation day the sacred *sadra* (shirt) and *kusti* (girdle) are put on for the first time. They will be worn at all times.

Considerations for the living
English may not be the first language for a Zoroastrian and interpretation may be required. Zoroastrianism requires a high standard of hygiene, and running water will be preferred for washing. A bowl of freshly drawn water is an acceptable alternative.

Daily prayers are fundamental. The sacred girdle is tied and untied during the *kusti* prayers, and very sick patients may need help to do this.

Diet
There are no general dietary restrictions but some Zoroastrians may not eat pork or beef and may prefer a vegetarian diet in hospital.

Care of the dying
Zoroastrians would wish to have their loved ones near at the time of death. Relatives, friends or, rarely, a Zoroastrian priest may say prayers. There are no last rites before death.

Post-mortems and body donation
Post-mortems are forbidden in religious law and would be refused except for coroner's cases. Body donation is likewise forbidden.

Blood transfusion and transplants
Orthodox Zoroastrians consider that pollution of the body is against the will of God. They will be against blood transfusion for this reason, probably being unwilling both to donate and to receive. Organ transplantation likewise introduces the concept of bodily or genetic pollution and is forbidden in strict religious law. Indeed, intermarriage itself is forbidden, to preserve the genetic purity of the Zoroastrian race. The less orthodox, however, may agree to some of these treatments.

Procedure at death
Routine last offices are appropriate. It is important that the body is bathed before being dressed in white clothing. Most families will provide a special *sadra* which is to be worn next to the skin under the shroud, with the sacred *kusti*. The family may wish the head to

---

Fill in appropriate local addresses and phone numbers

Zoroastrian temples

Funeral directors

Local cemeteries

---

be covered with a cap or scarf.

Traditionally, Zoroastrian funerals take place as soon as possible after death, as in the Jewish and Muslim faiths. Delay will cause distress, and any reason for it must be carefully explained to the family. Health-care staff can help to speed up the process.

Funerals
Zoroastrians believe that earth burial, cremation or disposal by water contaminates the sacred elements of earth, fire and water. In India, the Tower of Silence is the setting for disposal. This stone tower, outside the city, is built with three concentric circles, one each for men, women and children. It has no windows and no roof, and only certain bearers are allowed to enter. After ritual observances, the body is carried to the tower and left on the stone floor, exposed to the sun and the vultures, who strip the bones clean within a couple of hours. The sun-dried bones are later swept into the central well.

In the UK, other methods of disposal must be used. Family members may wish to prepare the body for the funeral, but in most cases a funeral director will be instructed. Funerals should take place as quickly as possible after death, either on the same day or on the next. In the UK both burial and cremation are accepted.

If a Zoroastrian patient has no immediate relatives or friends to attend his last illness, health-care staff can contact the address below for help: The Zoroastrian Trust Funds of Europe (Incorporated), Zoroastrian House, 88 Compayne Gardens, London NW6 3RU, tel: 071-328 6018.

FURTHER READING
Green, J.B., Green, M.A. *Dealing with Death: Practices and procedures*. London: Chapman and Hall, 1992.
Polson, C.J., Marshall, T.K. *The Disposal of the Dead*. London: English Universities Press, 1975.

RASTAFARIANISM

RASTAFARIANS are followers of a growing movement which began in the 1930s in the West Indies, mainly in Jamaica and Dominica, among the descendents of slave families who had come from Africa. Identification with Africa is central to the Rastafarian doctrine and the movement is linked to the roots of resistance to slavery. The 'Back to Africa' movement, led by Marcus Garvey (1887–1940) raised black consciousness and self-respect, and has inspired the faith.

The accession of Ras (Prince) Tafari as the Emperor of Ethiopia (Haile Selassie I) in 1930 is central to Rastafarian belief. He is considered to be a divine being, the Messiah of the human race, who will ultimately lead all black people to freedom. Believers claim there is a direct lineage from the biblical King David to Ras Tafari (hence the name Rastafarian). The Emperor also bears the titles of 'King of Kings' and the 'Lion of Judah'.

The Rastafarian movement has rejected many aspects of the major cultural influences which were predominant in Jamaica, and has become a distinct entity. The Old and New Testaments are still regarded as scriptures, but Rastafarians do not consider themselves to be Christians. For them, Christ's spirit has been reborn in Ras Tafari, the new Messiah. Rastafarians believe that they are the true Jews, who will eventually be redeemed by repatriation to Africa, their true home and heaven on earth.

Rastafarianism is a personal religion. There are no church buildings, set services or official clergy. All members share in the religious aspects, have a

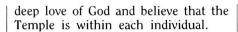

deep love of God and believe that the Temple is within each individual.

Considerations for the living

Rastafarians will be unwilling to receive any treatment which might contaminate the body, and some may reject Western-style treatments. Some will prefer to try alternative therapies such as herbalism, or acupuncture. However, those who seek the advice of doctors are likely to accept some conventional treatment.

Members of the faith are readily identified by their distinctive hairstyles. 'Dreadlocks' or 'locks' are a symbol of the faith and a sign of black pride. Orthodox members may not permit their hair to be cut.

Rastafarian women dress modestly at all times, and this must be respected in hospital. There is a taboo on the wearing of second-hand clothing, and orthodox patients may be unwilling to wear hospital garments which have been worn by others. Disposable theatre gowns may be preferred.

Visiting the sick is important. Visits are often made in groups which is sometimes frowned on by hospital staff. Rastafarian visitors therefore often feel they are made unwelcome in the hospital environment.

Diet

All forms of pig meat are forbidden. Some feel that all meat is unnecessary and follow a vegetarian diet. Certain fish are regarded as unwholesome; herring and sardines, among others, are not acceptable.

Care of the dying

The family may pray by the bedside of a dying member, but other than this there are no last rites. Rastafarians believe in the resurrection of the soul after death, but not of the flesh.

Post-mortems and body donation

Both would be extremely distasteful to most Rastafarians. Few would agree to a post-mortem except where it is ordered by the coroner.

Blood transfusion

The fear of contamination of the body will influence the attitude to transfusion. Assurance will be needed that no disease will be transmitted. Objection may be raised to both donation and reception, although donation to, and reception from, other members of the family may be considered.

Organ transplants

Again, the fear of contamination will make willing participation unlikely. There is also a belief that to do so is to interfere with God's plan for mankind.

Procedure at death

Routine last offices are appropriate.

Funerals

Burial is preferred but cremation is not forbidden. The funeral is plain and simple, unlike the elaborate occasions seen in the funerals of other Afro-Caribbean groups. It will be attended by only the intimate family and friends. There is no special mourning ritual, but family and friends are very supportive of the bereaved.

FURTHER READING
Campbell, H. *Rasta and Resistance*. London: Hansib Publishing, 1985.
Green, J.B., Green, M.A. *Dealing with Death: Practices and procedures*. London: Chapman and Hall, 1992.

Fill in appropriate local addresses and phone numbers

Funeral directors

Local cemeteries

THE AFRO-CARIBBEAN COMMUNITY

THERE is in reality no such concept as a single Afro-Caribbean community, but some cultural and traditional patterns are likely to be common among those with roots in the Caribbean islands. The main religion of the Caribbean islands (the West Indies) is some form of Christianity, but different island communities have differing religious backgrounds and wide variations in their ritual practice.

The major Christian churches in the Afro-Caribbean community are Anglican, Methodist and Pentecostal and among the older generations, a high proportion of followers are church attenders. The church is a social and community centre as well as a religious one. (The growing and distinct movement of Rastafarianism is considered next week.)

In the UK, the religious background of an Afro-Caribbean community will reflect the culture of the island from which its members came. At death, religious differences are likely to be minimised, and cultural and island identity predominate.

On the whole these communities are likely to be more demonstrative in the practice of religion than their Caucasian counterparts. For example, Afro-Caribbean Methodists regard baptism as very important, and the baptismal service for a child is a major religious occasion for his or her family and friends.

Frequently, parents do not marry, and they may not even live together. Grandparents are central in family relationships and often play a major part in the rearing of grandchildren. The extended family structure may be complex, but the family influence is strong, good relations are maintained and the family comes together at the death of one of its members. Most of the younger members of the Afro-Caribbean community were born in the UK, and the Caribbean influence may be less strong for them than for their parents and grandparents.

Considerations for the living
Sick patients in hospital would wish to be treated in the same way as everyone else and are unlikely to make special requests. Families may feel that the doctors are remote and unapproachable and feel unable to communicate with them and ask questions. Afro-Caribbean nursing staff may be able to help to bridge that gap.

Prayer is important for those who are regular churchgoers and the opportunity of privacy for prayer, and even for the singing of hymns, would be appreciated. Families would like to be able to be more demonstrative than the average white family and often feel emotionally restricted and inhibited in hospitals in the UK. Ward staff should

anticipate the need for a side room for a dying patient.

Diet
There are no general dietary restrictions, but hospital food may seem very dull to long-stay patients. An occasional Caribbean dish would be greatly appreciated.

Care of the dying
Visitors are very important to the sick, not just family members but also church and community leaders. The extended family may wish to make frequent and prolonged visits, and close relatives will want to be present at the death. West Indian patients are likely to require facilities for more than the average number of visitors. It is important that the clergy visit and that prayers are said together. Sacraments are seen as less necessary than prayer, but some will wish to take Holy Communion.

Post-mortems and body donation
Older members of the community may believe that the body must be intact for the after-life and will be deeply offended by its disfigurement. They are unlikely to give consent for post-mortem except for coroner's cases.

Blood transfusion
There is no religious objection to the giving or receiving of blood (except for Jehovah's Witnesses or Rastafarians).

Organ transplants
There is no religious objection to the reception of a transplanted organ, but those with belief in the sanctity of the body are unlikely to agree to organ donation. Younger family members may have different views.

Local addresses and phone numbers

Churches

Funeral directors

Cemeteries

Procedure at death
Routine last offices are appropriate. There are no religious objections to others handling the body as long as respect is shown. It may be preferred if a nurse from a similar ethnic background is able to fulfil this duty.

If death occurs at home, the laying out may be done by family and friends.

Funerals
In the UK, burial is the preferred method of disposal. The funeral is an important and elaborate occasion for the extended family and for all those who loved the deceased during life.

The entire community will wish to attend. Time will be allowed for the dispersed relatives to gather together. The body may be brought to the home before the funeral service, and may be viewed there and also during the singing of a hymn in church. This is a sign of respect, according to the wishes of the family, especially in Pentecostal communities. (The body should ideally be embalmed, especially if the funeral will be delayed.)

Because of the importance attached to funerals, time off work to attend them is necessary for many people, not just the very close family. The funeral service may be long, varied to suit the individual and characterised by hymns, tributes, a choir, a steel band or other music, gospel-singing and flowers.

At the graveside the family will fill the grave in themselves, while the singing continues. The congregation will probably return to the church hall for a gathering, after which the family house remains 'open' for people to call on the relatives, and for prayer, for about a week.

RESOURCE LIST

Christianity
Where you are unsure what action you should or should
not take, you should contact your hospital chaplain
who will be able to advise you.

Christian Science
The District Manager
Christian Science Committee on Publication
for Great Britain and Ireland
108 Palace Gardens Terrace
London W8 4RT

Jehovah's Witnesses
The Medical Desk
The Watch Tower Bible and Tract Society
Watch Tower House
The Ridgeway
London NW7 1RN

The Mormon Church
In the event of there being no local Church of Jesus Christ of
Latter-Day Saints, you can write for advice to:
The Church of Jesus Christ of Latter-Day Saints
Public Communications/Special Affairs Department
50 East North Temple Street
Salt Lake City
Utah 84150
USA

Zoroastrianism
The Zoroastrian Trust Funds of Europe (incorporated)
Zoroastrian House
88 Compayne Gardens
London NW6 3RU

Rastafarianism
As there is no formal church associated with this religion, you
may wish to contact appropriate local community leaders if there
are no friends or relatives who can advise you.

The Afro-Caribbean Community
The hospital chaplain or appropriate local churches should be
able to provide advice.